PLANTS VS. ZOMBIES™

TIMEPOCALYPSE

Written by **PAUL TOBIN**
Art by **RON CHAN**
Colors by **MATTHEW J. RAINWATER**
Letters by **STEVE DUTRO**
Cover by **RON CHAN**

DARK HORSE BOOKS

Publisher **MIKE RICHARDSON**
Editor **PHILIP R. SIMON**
Assistant Editor **ROXY POLK**
Designer **KAT LARSON**
Digital Production **CHRISTINA McKENZIE**

Special thanks to **LEIGH BEACH, SHANA DOERR,
A.J. RATHBUN, KRISTEN STAR, BRENNAN TOWNLEY,
JEREMY VANHOOZER**, and everyone at PopCap Games.

Nerd Block edition: January 2015
ISBN 978-1-61655-854-3

10 9 8 7 6 5 4 3 2 1
Printed in Canada

DarkHorse.com | PopCap.com

▷ No plants were harmed in the making of this comic. Numerous zombies
from various time periods, however, definitely were.

This volume collects *Plants vs. Zombies: Timepocalypse* #1–#6, originally serialized by Dark Horse Digital. | Published
by Dark Horse Books, a division of Dark Horse Comics, Inc., 10956 SE Main Street, Milwaukie, OR 97222 | International
Licensing: (503) 905-2377 | To find a comics shop in your area, call the Comic Shop Locator Service toll-free at 1-888-
266-4226. | **PLANTS vs. ZOMBIES: TIMEPOCALYPSE.** Plants vs. Zombies © 2014, 2015 Electronic Arts Inc. Plants vs.
Zombies and PopCap are trademarks of Electronic Arts Inc. All rights reserved. Dark Horse Books® and the Dark Horse
logo are registered trademarks of Dark Horse Comics, Inc. All rights reserved. No portion of this publication may be
reproduced or transmitted, in any form or by any means, without the express written permission of Dark Horse Comics,
Inc. Names, characters, places, and incidents featured in this publication either are the product of the author's imagination
or are used fictitiously. Any resemblance to actual persons (living or dead), events, institutions, or locales, without satiric
intent, is coincidental.

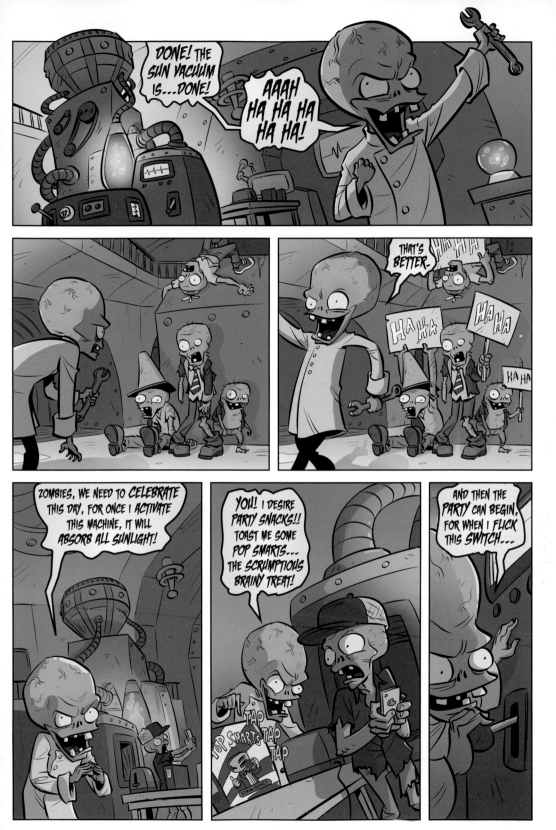

5

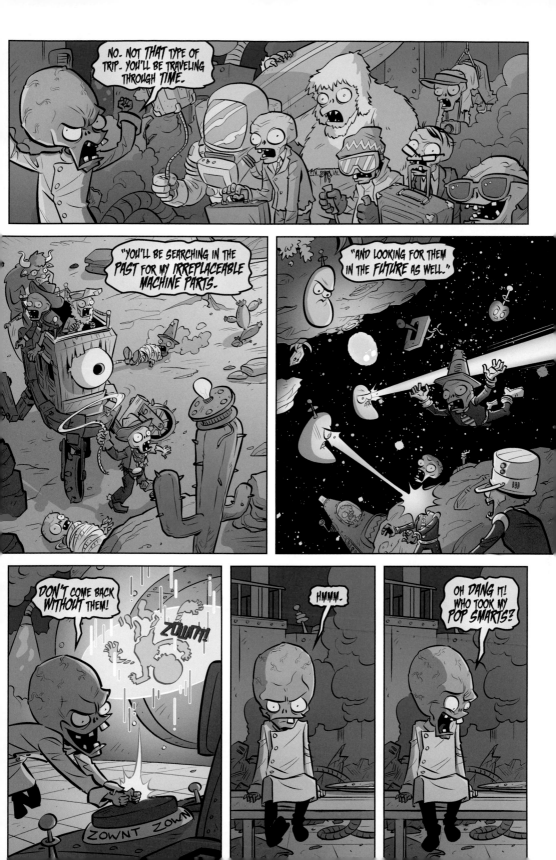

SERIOUSLY, THE *FIRST THING* YOU THOUGHT OF WAS *DINOSAURS* WITH *JETPACKS?*

PATRICE, LET ME TELL YOU A *SECRET.* DINOSAURS WITH JETPACKS IS...

...ALWAYS THE *FIRST THING* I'M THINKING OF.

PHUUTT!

AHHHH!

THUNKK!

HUH? WHAT'S THIS?

SOME SORT OF *ENGINE PIECE?* OR...UH...A *BROKEN ROBOT?* OR, MAYBE--

SLORKK

!!!

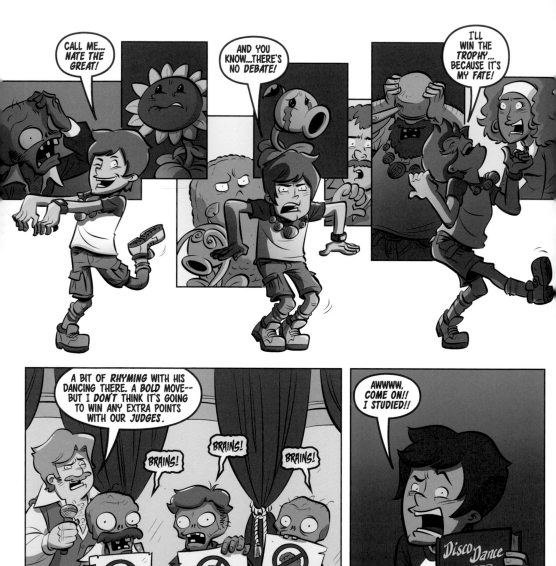

NEXT UP--REGINALD CAREFREE WINTHROP WORTHINGTON THE TWELFTH!

GRAAAH!

DANCE

CLAP! CLAP! CLAP! CLAP!

DANCE DANCE

CLAP! CLAP! CLAP!

CLAP! CLAP!

OHHHH....

DANCE

DANCE

THIS IS BAD. THE JUDGES ARE *LOVING* HIS *RADICALLY SMOOTH* DISCO MOVES.

BUT WE *NEED* TO WIN THAT *MACHINE PART*!

FLONG TONGLE!

TURN

COOL! NOW WE HAVE THREE OF THE MACHINE PARTS, BUT WE NEED THE OTHERS!

WHERE TO NOW?

LOP-LING YOGURT RATTLE REX!

HMMM. UNCLE DAVE WANTS US TO STEP OUTSIDE.

OUTSIDE? DID WE ALREADY TRAVEL THROUGH TIME?

STEP

THOOINK!

OFFHAND, I'D SAY... YES.

UH...OH...

WOW.

WELL, I GUESS EVERYTHING WAS BIGGER IN THE AGE OF DINOSAURS.

32

35

41

UH-OH.

ZOMBIES!

WE NEED TO STOP THEM BEFORE THEY CAN ALERT DR. ZOMBOSS ABOUT--

ZOMBOSS ALERT BUTTON

NOT DURING NAPTIME, PLEASE

PUSH!

OOPS.

ZZ ZK

ZKRS

ZRAKK!

BLOW!

WHOOOOSH!

NICE! WE'RE MAKING GOOD SPEED!

I'M HOPING WE CAN REACH EYE ISLAND BEFORE CHESTBEARD COMES BACK FOR HIS TREASURE.

"BECAUSE HIS MEN ARE A *TRAINED* GROUP OF *SKILLED* FIGHTERS. *HARD* TO BEAT. PLUS, THEY DON'T *SHOWER* VERY OFTEN. HARD TO *STOMACH*.

"AND OF COURSE WE NEED TO WORRY ABOUT THE *ZOMBIE NAVY*. THEY'RE NOT WELL TRAINED--OR ALL THAT *SMART*--BUT THERE'S *SO MANY* OF THEM THAT THEY BECOME DANGEROUS!"

BRAINS?

Please Take a Number

BRAINS?

93! WHO HAS NUMBER 93? 93 GETS TO SWING NEXT!

BRAINS?

BRAINS?

BROB-GOBBLE FRENK JOBBLY-POOF!

OKAY, UNCLE DAVE SAYS HE HAS *ALL* THE PARTS TO THE SUN VACUUM! IF WE GIVE HIM SOME *TIME*, HE CAN CHANGE IT AROUND...

"...SO THAT INSTEAD OF *DRAINING* THE SUN'S POWER, *VACUUMING* IT UP THE WAY ZOMBOSS *INTENDED* THE MACHINE TO BE USED..."

YES! YES!

"...WE CAN USE IT TO *MAGNIFY* THE SUN'S RAYS...GIVING THE PLANTS EVEN *MORE* POWER."

NO! NO! NO!

BUT...*WHILE* DAVE IS FINISHING HIS WORK ON THE MACHINE, HE WONDERS IF WE COULD DO HIM A FEW *FAVORS*.

SURE! WHAT'S HE NEED?

OKAY...FIRST HE NEEDS THE TOE-MASSAGING SHOES HE INVENTED, AND WE HAVE TO MOVE THE TELEVISION IN HERE SO THAT HE CAN WATCH HIS *PANDORA'S PLANTS* SOAP OPERA...

...AND HE'D LIKE SOME LEMONADE WITH ICE CUBES IN THE SHAPE OF BUNNIES... AND TWO FISHING POLES, HIS ROLLER SKATES...

...A SUNFLOWER THAT CAN PLAY THE DRUMS, AND...

...IN ORDER TO GIVE HIM *TIME* TO *FINISH* THE WORK, HE'D *REALLY* APPRECIATE IT...

Paul Tobin

Ron Chan

Matthew J. Rainwater

CREATOR BIOS

PAUL TOBIN is a critically acclaimed bald guy who had his first encounter with zombies when he watched the 1973 film *Children Shouldn't Play with Dead Things* on late-night television during one of the first times his parents ever left him alone. They returned to find him cowering in the kitchen with a knife. Paul eventually recovered enough mental stability to go on to write hundreds of comics for Marvel, DC, Dark Horse, and many others, including creator-owned titles such as *Colder* and *Bandette*, as well as *Prepare to Die!*—his debut novel. Paul's favorite zombie-fighting plants are the Cattail, the Snow Pea, and the Spikerock.

RON CHAN is a cartoonist, storyboard artist, and illustrator born and raised in Portland, Oregon. He graduated from the Savannah College of Art and Design in 2005, and is now a member of the Portland-based art collective Periscope Studio. His comic-book work has been published by Dark Horse, Marvel, and Image Comics, and storyboarding work of his includes boards for 3-D animation, gaming, internal development, user-experience design, and advertising for clients such as Microsoft, Amazon Kindle, Nike, and Sega. He really likes drawing the Bonk Choy.

Residing in the cool, damp forests of Portland, Oregon, **MATTHEW J. RAINWATER** is a freelance illustrator whose work has been featured in advertising, web design, and independent video games. On top of this, he also self-publishes several comic books, including *Garage Raja* and *Trailer Park Warlock*, both of which can be found at MattJRainwater .com. Matt is knee deep into *Plants vs. Zombies 2* but has yet to venture into the Far Future and Dark Ages worlds. His favorite zombie-bashing strategy utilizes a line of Bonk Choy with a Wall-nut front guard and Threepeater covering fire.

MORE DARK HORSE ALL-AGES TITLES

AW YEAH COMICS! AND . . . ACTION!

Cornelius and Alowicious are just your average comic book store employees, but when trouble strikes, they are . . . Action Cat and Adventure Bug! Join their epic all-ages adventures as they face off—with the help of Adorable Cat and Shelly Bug—against their archnemesis, Evil Cat, and his fiendish friends!

ISBN 978-1-61655-558-0 | $12.99

USAGI YOJIMBO

In his latest adventure, the rabbit *ronin* Usagi finds himself caught between competing gang lords fighting for control of a town called Hell, confronting a *nukekubi*—a flying cannibal head—and crossing paths with the demon Jei!

Volume 25: Fox Hunt
ISBN 978-1-59582-726-5 | $16.99

Volume 26: Traitors of the Earth | $16.99
ISBN 978-1-59582-910-8

Volume 27: A Town Called Hell | $16.99
ISBN 978-1-59582-970-2

AGE OF REPTILES OMNIBUS

When Ricardo Delgado first set his sights on creating comics, he crafted an eplc tale about the most unlikely cast of characters: dinosaurs. Since that first Eisner-winning foray into the world of sequential art he has returned to his critically acclaimed *Age of Reptiles* again and again, each time crafting a captivating saga about his saurian subjects.

ISBN 978-1-59582-683-1 | $24.99

ANGELIC LAYER BOOK 1

Junior-high student Misaki Suzuhara just arrived in Tokyo to live with her TV-star aunt and attend the prestigious Eriol Academy. But what excites Misaki most is Angelic Layer—an arena game where you control a miniature robot fighter with your mind! Can Misaki's enthusiasm and skill take her to the top of the arena?

ISBN 978-1-61655-021-9 | $19.99